Gran was visiting.
"Let's go to the park!" she said.

In the park Biff spotted a stone with a hole in it.

"From now on this is my lucky stone," she said with a big grin.

Biff kept the stone in her pocket.

She went on the swings.

She did a cartwheel.

She did a handstand.

Then it was time to go home.
"Wait!" said Biff. "I have lost my good luck stone!"

“Did you drop it?” said Chip.
“I must have,” said Biff with
a frown.

They went back to hunt for it.
Chip had a look under a shrub.

"Now I am all dirty!" he said.

Kipper had a look under the trees.

“Oh no!” he said. “A branch has torn my shirt!”

Gran had a look near the flowers.

“Ow!” she said. “A stinging nettle!
I have been stung!”

“Wait!” said Biff. “The stone was in my right pocket, *not* the left!”

“I never lost it after all!” she said.

“See? I said it was a lucky stone!”